The cartoons in this book are

for **whatever** you want to do with them. No royalties,
no charges, no fees, no two-drink minimum, **no nothing!**

Use them free in your newspaper, magazine, newsletter, book, presentation,
CD-ROM, T-shirt; whatever you want. There are no restrictions!

Use one cartoon or use them all. There is no limit!

Sell them, trade them, lease them, or give them away.
You can even make copies for others to use.

All I ask in return is that you include **The Borderline, by Gabe Martin**, and **borderln@cts.com** (from the
title page) on each cartoon that you use. You get free cartoons and I get free exposure for my stuff.
What a deal!

This free cartoon offer is good until 9/9/99 as stated on the license on the next page.

THE BORDERLINE FREE-CARTOON LICENSE AGREEMENT

In the context of this agreement "you" shall refer to any individual, group, organization, or corporate, public, or private entity. This license is transferable.

PART I - GRANT

The Borderline hereby grants you a non-exclusive license to use, free of charge, the cartoons in this book (**"Oooo... bit your tongue?"**) You may use the cartoons in the manner described in Part II below under "Scope of Grant".

PART II - SCOPE OF GRANT

You may:

1) Reproduce unlimited copies of the cartoons.
2) Freely distribute copies of the cartoons for purposes of sale, rental, lease, or lending.
3) Publicly display copies of the cartoons.

You may not:

1) Modify the cartoons or create a derivative work of any cartoon except to proportionally scale or convert to electronic media.
2) Use any cartoon without also including the title information (i.e., **"The Borderline"**, **"by Gabe Martin"**, and **"borderln@cts.com"**) with each cartoon.

TITLE: Title, ownership rights, and intellectual property rights in the cartoons shall remain in The Borderline except as indicated under "Scope of Grant" above.

TERMINATION: This license shall termindate automatically on September 9, 1999 unless extended in writing by The Borderline. On termination, copying, distributing, and public display of the cartoons will no longer be permitted without prior written permission from The Borderline.

"Ooooh... bit your tongue?"

The
BORDERLINE ™

By Gabe Martin

E-mail: borderln@cts.com   Web: http://www.the-borderline.com
(Syndicator, Distributor, Publisher, Retailer inquires welcome - 1-800-877-5331)

Borderline Publishing Ink.
San Diego, CA U.S.A.

E-mail: borderln@cts.com   Web: http://www.the-borderline.com
(Syndicator, Distributor, Publisher, Retailer inquires welcome - 1-800-877-5331)

Dedicated to my loving Mother, who carried me, spoon-fed me, dressed me, bathed me, and changed my diapers up until about a few months ago, when I came out of the coma.

Thanks, Mom.

(I just wanted everyone to know that my son was never really in a coma. - Gabe's Mom)

This page left unintentionally blank.

Delaware, Christmas 1776: General Washington and his men wait for the signal.

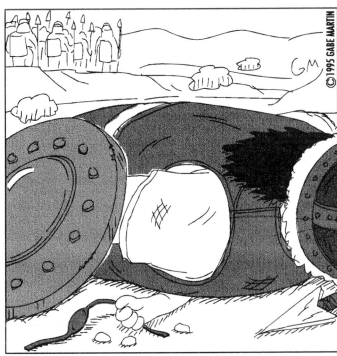

**935 B.C.: David becomes the first to realize that, actually, the bigger they are, the harder they fall--
...on you.**

"So! You're a homing pigeon, are you? You can find your own way back, can you? For heaven's sake, Warren, can't you for once just stop and *ask for directions?!*"

"I'm sorry Mr. Hallerson, but I'm afraid we can't help you. And frankly, I don't think *anyone* will be willing to help you."

Since Mr. Hodges insisted on pronouncing it "ro-but", his students insisted on their own spelling for Mr. Hodges' class.

The Dog and the Rooster would have continued to live together in perfect harmony, if only the Rooster hadn't burned his finger on the stove one day.

"Hey Zark, you baboon brain! No stand under long-neck in lightning storm!"

Only seconds after the first bell, the highly publicized "Wrestling Match of the Century" falls flat on it's face.

June 24, 1626: For the third time that month, Running Bear, chief of the Manhattan Indians, prepares to "sell" his island to yet another unsuspecting white man tribe.

"Jerry you idiot! Can't you read?!"

After his luck changed at the slots, Scott decided to go where the _big_ money was.

Niche marketing strikes out.

"Honey, wake up! What's that noise downstairs?"

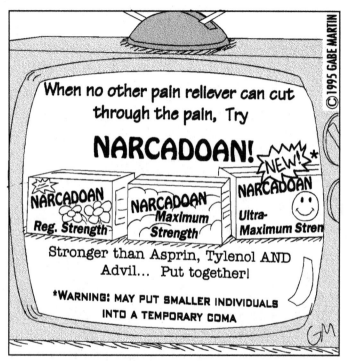

Pharmaceutical One-Up-Manship

Doug now realized that he never should've fallen asleep before take-off.

After 5 years on the job and 50,000 repetitions of "Pop Goes the Weasel", Harry finally goes "pop".

Larry dreamed of becoming a millionaire, but every two weeks he got his reality check.

Why Rome was sacked so many times.

Yet another corporation tries to cash in on a Southern California fad.

Arachnid Singles Bars

" Oh for crying out loud! Not 'Barbara Ann' again! "

17

Richard Simmons double-deals on his Deal-A-Meal.

Late that night, Vince suddenly realizes why, oddly,
he hadn't seen any roaches in his new apartment.

"C'mon Baby, would I steer you wrong?"

Fish Suicide Threats

"Oh, just ignore her. She's just trying for sympathy."

"The accountants just got their computers installed, but Fred still insists on having all his forms in triplicate."

Elliott finally got fed up and decided that "From now on, nobody touches nobody!"

Right then and there, Randy vows to never buy
Saran Wrap again.

"I've found the problem, Ma'am, and you were right: it just doesn't like you."

Shortly after the release of "*Lotus 1-2-3*", IBM attempted to market it's largely ignored competitor program.

Mathematician Memory Devices

Even fifty years after the "Singapore Incident",
Michael Fay still felt a twinge of pain every
time he passed by this part of the mall.

In the Monkey Business World

New Age Electronics

"Walter, I want you to have a talk with your son-- he's got a job, his own apartment, he doesn't borrow money-- I mean, it's just not *normal,* for crying out loud!"

"Your Holiness-- It's the 'Red Phone' !"

Slowly, Tony began to realize that his Poker Face was no match for Bob's Baby Face or Larry's Smiley Face.

Rex, the All-Seeing-Eye-Dog.

Mike's new screen was perhaps a bit too sensitive.

28

"Well, looks like the end of summer's coming."

Desperate to feed his ever-increasing addiction,
the Rabbit turns to committing grand-theft TRIX.

In one of those ironic twists of fate, everyone **but** Jerry the propboy was to have a very, *very* Merry Christmas that year.

Cruise Missiles on a Friday Night

"Bernie, you fool! Serpentine! Serpentine!!"

Fred had wanted to buy the car that same day, but he had heard that you should always sleep on it first.

Feeling for the "Uh-oh" button, Steve unknowingly was about to end his brief carreer as sit-com sound-effects man.

Facing a publication deadline, Art hastily evaluates
how well Warp stacks up against Windows '95.

Frank finally got the hang of seeing the 3-D pictures,
but the problem was now the rest of the world
looked 2-D.

Frank begins to seriously question which is worse--
death or taxes.

Father's Day over at Father Time's place.

Circa 426: Saint Patrick drives the snakes out of Ireland.

"There goes Lenny again-- he thinks he's king of all he surveys."

Steve's immune system picked the absolute worst
time to reject his new hair transplant.

Thack shows off his new stereo.

"Well, we're not exactly sure, but we think it's lettuce."

To boost sagging revenues, the Scottish Tourist Commission sponsors the first ever "**LOCH NESS MONSTER TRUCK RALLY!!!!!!**"

Larry didn't know where he was or how he'd got here, but he knew that he was in big trouble.

After running the slicing machine for 40 years, Dave just couldn't cut it anymore.

Test Nightmares

Bathroom Break at the New York Stock Exchange

Sneeze-guard or no sneeze-guard, Tony was bound and determined to get the last of the pepperoni.

The beginning of the end for the Pony Express.

41

Mario prayed that he would win just this one race, and maybe then he could get some better sponsors.

Super Hero Movie Rip-offs

How it all started.

Passing the time on Death Row.

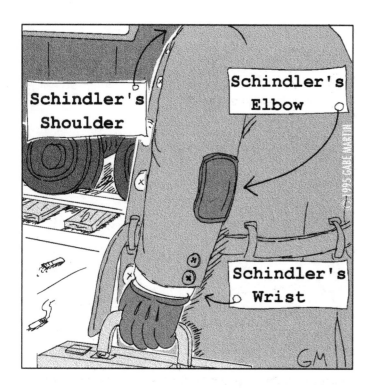

Geppetto knew that he should've never bought one of those electric pencil sharpeners.

The challenge of designing a fail-safe Space Shuttle.

Forever in the shadow of his "genius" older brother, the merely "smart" Alek Einstein found his name gain popularity only as ridicule.

How the Plains Indians viewed the early settlers.

"I don't care what they say-- I'm staying home."

46

**After having all his other approaches fail,
Bernie tries honesty.**

Wayne's first & last day working at the restaurant.

Each year, Steve had to keep reminding himself not to invite his vegetarian coworkers to his annual barbecue.

"Now this little baby here's a good model-- sure it's cheaper, but you get more big bang for your buck."

"Keep an eye on Harry-- when he gets too many drinks in him he starts to drink right out of the bowl."

50

Comic Book Theoriticians

For his lesser transgression, the dinner companion of Damocles was forced to sit under the lesser-known "Fork of Darnocles".

In a pathetic show of defiance, Frank momentarily breaks out of his couch-potato stupor and "touches that dial".

...If it had been "That's one small step for man, one giant trip for mankind".

Alien Economists

54

1847: After surviving the ill-fated winter crossing of the Sierra Nevada Mountains, George Donner opens a short-lived restaurant business.

Panic begins to set in as Herb realizes that dropping a roll hasn't helped.

55

"What is this?! You borrowed five bucks yesterday and you're broke already?! How--... hey wait a minute... You've been buying food, haven't you, Larry!"

"That does it, Johnson! I'm transferring you to the park Hindquarters!"

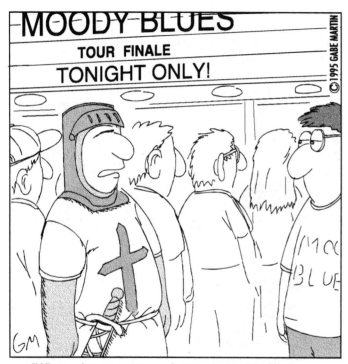

"Whoa-- bummer, man. Are you *sure* it's **Nights** In White Satin?"

Momentarily distracted, Herb fails to notice the silently approaching Lawn Shark.

58

"T'be sure, I'm here to see 'bout that Lighthouse keepin' job."

Sub-Atomic Talk-Show Disasters

With her productive days far behind her, Elsie the Cow couldn't help but see the latest milk ad campaign as nothing but a cruel joke.

Mozart's parents knew he was destined to become a great composer the minute they first saw his prominent treble cleft chin.

After years of searching, Walter finally found his niche.

"All returns must be accompanied by receipt and returned in their original packaging...."

In the dry deserts of the American Southwest, the early prospectors often resorted to "picking" their noses.

"Wait a minute, Jenkins-- that isn't blood-- it's red fingernail polish!"

President's Day Planner

Raiders of the Lost Refrigerator

Eventually, Darryl's mental name search took over all of his cognitive resources.

Ever since the millipedes moved in upstairs,
Bob kept losing a lot of sleep waiting for
the last shoe to fall.

How young Chief Sitting-In-Bull became famous.

"Y'know, he's so crazy he just might work."

"Ok men, pass this along-- this is our last chance, so at high noon we all make a break for it-- but *this* time, don't everybody all go running in the same direction!"

Minutes later, the solar scientists would realize that the odd sunspot pattern they were observing was, in fact, the immediate precursor to a supernova explosion.

67

Bob realized too late that he should have never taken a number.

"I'm sorry Mr. Thorogood, but you're bad to the bone--
b-b-b-b-b-bad."

Working on an anonymous tip, the police finally nab the notorious Tony "The Tagger" Tortelli.

In yet another close call for Superman's secret identity, Clark suddenly realizes that he had forgotten to *wear* a T-shirt that day.

After recent layoffs at the U.S. Robotics West Coast HQ, the remaining employees lived in constant fear wondering who would be terminated next.

"I'm sorry sir, you misunderstood. I said take the _witless_ stand."

After blowing out the candles with his nose, Duane pretty much had the whole cake to himself.

Although he'd just read the book cover-to-cover,
Frank was now more confused than ever.

"Excuse me Mr. Mistry, I know that you're the new owner of the company and all, but as your senior VP, I would strongly advise you to go back to the company's old name."

73

When multi-tasking breaks down.

Bob knew he should learn to touch-type, but he'd gotten so used to the "Hunt & Peck" method.

During a break in the filming of their latest "King Kong vs. Godzilla" movie, the two stars pass the time with a game of pick-up trucks.

Centuries before Isaac Newton's discoveries, Polynesian mathmatician Pao Lau would have discovered the laws of gravity first... had he ever come out of the coma.

All the rest of the day, passing neighbors would wonder why Larry was standing motionless in his doorway, a can of beer in his hand.

Free-Range Chickens

When his Aunt Edna had asked him what he wanted for his birthday, Johnny sadly had forgotten that her hearing wasn't so good anymore.

Dan finally reached the end of his rope--
so he had to go back home.

If he hadn't needed the exercise so much, Santa
would've given up his summer-home garden
years ago.

Although extremely popular in '60's slang, "groovy" was the bane of songwriters of the era.

"Hang on, Zukerman-- we want to give the customers their money's worth. Handle that one a little longer."

"What's the matter? You look at me like I got one head."

"Hot enough for ya?"

Once again the pups were able to fool Old Trusty's failing sense of smell with the "fake vomit" gag.

After only 45 minutes in the United States, Hiroshu had already mastered using the knife and fork.

After being shipwrecked for 3 weeks with no food, Laurel finally decided to eat hearty.

Why they're called the OPPOSITE sexes.

Hangman Humor

"Gee-- I always thought it was just an expression."

Mobile Bay, August 5, 1864: Admiral Farragut wimps out.

Driving long into the night and far from the nearest town, Steve has a near-Death Valley experience.

"Hey! You didn't put any alcohol on my arm!"

1953: The structure of the DNA molecule is first described.

"Well now look what you've done! You just don't know when to quit, do you, Harold?! You just keep droning on and on, don't you, Harold?!"

When Vultures Eat Out

The REAL reason dinosaurs became extinct.
(With apologies to Gary Larson)

"Now hold it right there, buddy! I told you if you started something in _my_ town _I_ was gonna finish it-- Now gimmie that brush!"

Unknown to most historians, Ben Franklin's invention of the pot-bellied stove was preceded by his much-ridiculed beer-bellied stove.

How feeding frenzies start.

The Gingerbread Man's brief career as the mailman
of Candyland came to an abrupt end down at
Old Mother Hubbard's place.

When Nuclear Proliferation gets
out of hand.

Going down in poker history, Jake attempts to
cheat Death.

Trying his hand at creating a world-renowned salad like that of the Great Caesar, Old King Cole invariably ended up with just a bunch of soggy, shredded cabbage.

"Wait a minute-- you want to get one of these? Martha, you KNOW how these new-fangled coral beds bother my back."

Daniel in the Lion's Living Room

Largest number of men on a dead man's chest: **15**, (Aug. 24, 1708).

Stan didn't really mind the new keyboard design, but he just wished they hadn't put that new key so close to the "Enter".

"Well, the way we see it, we're just trying to improve the species diversity of the planet."

"Hey Elaine-- look what the cat just dragged in!"

"Well what the heck?! What's this?!"

95

"Buddy! How many times have I told you not to engulf your food?!"

While testing out his new cereal mix on his horse, Dave gets some unexpected feed-back.

Dan couldn't see how this would help his flu, but doctor's orders were doctor's orders.

On her way to the publisher, Mary Shelley stops for a bite of lunch, still vaguely unsatisfied with the title of her new novel mauscript, *Schmuckenstein.*

After Steve moved the cans to the front of his truck, he never again had problems with people getting in his way.

Suddenly, Bob realizes that he's "part of the problem".

Serial-Link Killers

"Hey Farmer Brown!!-- Go ahead... *make my hay!*"

As a colt, Henry never had any fun at the pool.

Little is known about Intel's first experimental micro-processor, other than it's reportedly limited capabilities.

As high noon drew near, the two combatants prepared to settle their long-standing rivalry once and for all.

Though once the life of the party, everybody had quickly grown tired of Ed and his one-trick knee.

"So-- how's the opportunity for advancement in this place?"

Southern California, circa 1790: Despite Saint Andreas' later protestations, everyone knew that it *was* his fault.

Anteater Mothers

Larry accidentally walks into one of those "A guy walks into a bar" jokes.

"Oh, stop being a baby and go back to bed-- and I don't want to hear another word about the "big" spider in your room, got it?!"

Deathly afraid of snakes, Joel always had to wear blinders while hiking.

Free from the buoyancy of the marsh, Bernie the Brontosaurus attempts to walk on land.

"Yes, I realize that, Mr. Holsen, but you can't list your home bathroom as a business deduction just because you do your business there."

"We're landing, Sir. Please stow your Carri-on."

Louise knew that she should've bought a Chia Pet
with papers.

No matter how hard Stanley tried, he just
couldn't forget.

New York Freeway Signage.

Mafia Florists

"Ooo0! You really whacked that one good, Henderson!"

After the Senators finished raking the tobacco
company executives over the coals,
they started on Haagen Dazs.

"I don't believe it! They've humanized me again!"

Dazed and confused, the villagers glanced around the club, amazed to have survived but unaware that they had just inadvertantly been bombed back to the Jazz Age.

Hell's Kitchen

...And **everywhere** that Mary went, the lamb was sure to go....

After asking "When's Dinner?" for the fifth time, Jerry finds out that sometimes the "squeaky wheel" gets the lard.

"Why, in my day we sometimes had to fly 30 miles before we could find a car to go on."

Three-Dog Nightmare

As an ironic end to his career, Travis' Cheatin' Heart suffers an Achy-breaky Heart attack.

Asexual Harassment

"Now gentlemen, in this computer-enhanced enlargment of the famous frame #36059, you can clearly see a shadowy figure on the grassy knoll. A second gunman? Who knows."

Um, B-5.

You can't call that one. That one sinks my carrier.

After he got married, Hank didn't even get to call the shots in Battleship.

"Oh great! Look who's just moved in next door-- a
family of Bumbling Bees!"

After his subtler methods of getting the new class'
attention had failed, Mr. Johnson decided it was time
for his "not-so-subtle" methods.

Through a machine malfunction at the General Mills factory, styrofoam chunks are accidentally substituted for the marshmallow pieces--- and nobody notices.

Internet-In-a-Chatterbox

August 29, 1997-- 7:43 am: Wayne Lorenzoski's coffee maker becomes self-aware.

Unfortunately for Dave, the police dogs had only a very limited vocabulary.

How all those cereals "stay crispy in milk".

"Well, that finishes me... I guess it's like my pappy always said-- you can't beat a dead horse."

"Be careful what you say to Jerry... he's always so self-defensive."

Insect Comic Strips

"Engines!!!"

Desperate for a campaign slogan in his first presidential bid, Franklin D. Roosevelt retreats to a local bar to gather his thoughts.

Frog Fast Food

Even in the afterlife, Al could never even make it past Cloud 1.

Street corner competition

123

June 25, 1776: **Thomas Jefferson submits his first draft of the Declaration of Independence to George Washington.**

Pangaea, 200 Million B.C.: The first dinosurs appear.

Fred's job was a lot less frustrating ever since he customized his DOOM game.

Ever since he had his name legally changed, Narl found himself in one comedic situation after another.

Larry is stumped-- Already.

"Careful, Sven. It isn't over til the fat lady sinks."

"Hey Boss? Rocky. Well, we'z did like ya told us...
It took a few sleeping pills, but we did it."

As the years drug on, Skywalker began to find
Obi-Wan increasingly annoying.

And just yesterday, Mike had wondered if things could possibly get any more cynical.

The bitter turf war became all-out when Jack Frost tried to "ice" Old Man Winter once and for all by hiring the notorious "Frosty the Hitman".

God's Refrigerator

Remember: Guns and alcohol don't mix!
(This has been a federally mandated public
service anouncement.)

"Y'know, I was wrong. You really look like a fool behind the wheel of this sports car."

In the huddle, before playbooks and Delay-Of-Game penalties.

For the first time, the head of the Jamaican Tourist Board really took the time to read their new slogan out-loud.

"We think he went in here-- now remember, boys... he's a killer."

Another Kodiak moment

Seconds after Moon-Watcher's discovery, the tribe's entire theological perspective was suddenly turned upside-down.

Another reason Las Vegas somehow still manages
to pay its electric bill.

Another unwary consumer falls for the "*ALL U CAN
EAT FOR 99¢ BREAKFAST SPECIAL*".

After enduring 23 years of Bob's forgetfulness
Harriet abandons all subtlety.

Luigi would've never sold him the balloons had he
known that the guy was another one of those
"balloon-animal rights" wackos.

"It looks like you're perfect for the job, Mr. Barney, but I think we're gonna have to do something about those teeth."

Translation: "I came, I saw, I conquered, I had a beer!!"

Like many "at risk" inner-city kids, he eventually turned to crime and ended up being sent to the Big Bird House.

Albert Einstein & Satyendra Bose's first attempt to produce the elusive fourth state of matter, the Bose-Einstein Milk Condensate, disappointingly ended with cottage cheese splattered all over the lab.

136